all my
Love
Lauren
Jenkins

## ESSEX VOL I

Edited by
Michelle Warrington

First published in Great Britain in 1998 by
*POETRY NOW YOUNG WRITERS*
1-2 Wainman Road, Woodston,
Peterborough, PE2 7BU
Telephone (01733) 230748

HB ISBN 0 75430 189 3
SB ISBN 0 75430 190 7

# FOREWORD

With over 63,000 entries for this year's Cosmic competition, it has proved to be our most demanding editing year to date.

We were, however, helped immensely by the fantastic standard of entries we received, and, on behalf of the Young Writers team, thank you.

*Cosmic Essex Vol I* is a tremendous reflection on the writing abilities of 8 & 9 year old children, and the teachers who have encouraged them must take a great deal of credit.

We hope that you enjoy reading *Cosmic Essex Vol I* and that you are impressed with the variety of poems and style with which they are written, giving an insight into the minds of young children and what they think about the world today.

# CONTENTS

Nightingale Primary School

| | | |
|---|---|---|
| | Amy Allen | 13 |
| | Preeti Sohota | 13 |

Oaklands School

| | | |
|---|---|---|
| | Sophie Wise | 14 |
| | Maria Green | 15 |
| | Natasha Panasiuk | 16 |
| | Elleni Kyriakides | 16 |
| | Emma Reeves | 17 |
| | Semona Auluk | 18 |
| | Gemma Torgut | 18 |
| | Lauren Jenkin | 19 |

St Alban's RC School

| | | |
|---|---|---|
| | Loren O'Connell | 19 |
| | Emily Harrison | 20 |
| | Colin Campbell | 20 |
| | Tom Vargas | 21 |
| | Harry Tyler | 21 |
| | Kathleen Gillespie | 21 |
| | Emma Furzer | 22 |

St Mary's RC JMI School

| | | |
|---|---|---|
| | Abigail Garrard | 22 |
| | Amy Falvey-Browne | 23 |
| | Emma Stacey | 23 |
| | Gregory Hanshaw | 24 |
| | Lianne Shanley | 24 |
| | Francesca Anastasio | 25 |
| | Jamie Cannell | 25 |
| | Keiran Lloyd Jones | 26 |
| | Liam Cox | 26 |
| | Alexander Miller | 27 |
| | Luke Sampayo | 27 |
| | Warren James | 27 |
| | Jessica Dodd | 28 |
| | Jamie Jones | 29 |

Springfield PNEU School

Thames View Junior School

| | |
|---|---|
| Donna Cracknell | 66 |
| Amy Stone | 67 |
| Michael Kemp | 67 |
| Tom Manning | 68 |
| Anthony Spurr Jr | 68 |
| Rachel Wheeler | 68 |
| Jade Trowbridge | 69 |
| Dhanya Pratheep | 70 |
| Deborah Stevens | 70 |
| Frankie Robinson | 70 |
| Stella Arenillas | 71 |
| Nikki Tolley | 71 |
| Jay Kristiansen | 71 |
| Luke Veazey | 72 |
| Matthew Webb | 72 |
| Connie Taylor | 72 |
| Misha Trumpet | 73 |
| Katie Byrne | 73 |
| Daniel Jones | 74 |
| Patrick Kenny | 74 |
| Daniel Binder | 74 |
| Lucy May Guest | 75 |
| Josiah Oyekunle | 75 |
| Joe Cunningham | 76 |
| Kayleigh Gargan | 76 |
| Ricky Marney | 77 |
| Simon Harris | 77 |
| Shane Smith | 77 |
| Johnita Francis | 78 |
| Ryan Mills-Smith | 78 |
| Kay Jarvis | 79 |
| George McLaughlin | 79 |
| Billy Ellis | 79 |

Theydon Bois CP School

| | |
|---|---|
| Rachel Wright | 80 |
| Rebecca Wheeler | 80 |

| | |
|---|---|
| Laura Gabb | 81 |
| Jack White | 81 |
| James Gooch | 82 |
| Robert Jones | 82 |
| Eleanor Gooch | 83 |
| Alexander Kirk | 83 |
| Nicholas Coe | 84 |
| Kimberley Bennett | 84 |
| Andrew Martin | 85 |
| Alex Venables | 85 |
| James Brough | 86 |
| Nicola Knight | 86 |
| Jonathan Cooper | 87 |
| Ben Buisson | 87 |
| Charlotte Roll | 88 |
| Christopher Grosvenor | 88 |
| Glenn Jobling | 89 |
| Matthew McDonald | 89 |
| Emma Bateman | 90 |
| Charlotte Debenham | 90 |
| Elizabeth Ashton | 91 |
| Anna Jobling | 91 |
| Jamie Macpherson | 92 |
| Carol Meteyard | 93 |
| Joe Quill | 94 |
| Adam Nicoll | 94 |
| Sarah Jones | 95 |
| Jenna Dodd | 95 |
| Georgina Rutter | 96 |
| Hayley Jones | 96 |
| Matthew Curtis | 97 |
| Thomas Rendell | 97 |
| Emma Suckling | 98 |
| Rebecca Bales | 99 |
| Lucy Mason | 99 |
| Louise Nunn | 100 |
| Charlotte Davey | 100 |
| Ben Pearce | 101 |

# THE POEMS

## ALIENS

Some aliens are purple with orange spots,
And some are completely see-through with green blots.
Some have wings for transportation
And some have rocket packs to whiz around orbit.
Some aliens have inter-galactic laser guns
And some have laser beams that come out their eyes.
Some aliens have one or three eyes,
And some have trillions of eyes,
But an alien's an alien and that's that.

*Michael Myers  (9)*
*Grove Junior School*

## MOON MOON

Moon moon
What a sight
Sky sky
Black and white
Sun sun
High and bright
Birds birds
Fly at night
Spaceship spaceship
Gives a fright
I think it's time to turn out the light.

*Lauren Judd  (9)*
*Grove Junior School*

## I WISH I COULD GO TO THE MOON

I wish I could go to the moon,
To see all the stars,
I wish I could go to the moon,
And to see Mars.

I wish I could go to the moon,
As it is so bright,
I wish I could go to the moon,
Every single night.

I wish I could go to the moon,
To see if someone is there,
I wish I could go to the moon,
I wonder if they would care.

*Lauren Standen  (9)*
*Grove Junior School*

## NETBALL

Nerve-racking playing
Even when you're practising
Trying to score

Ball in your hands. What next?
A goal! *Yes!*
Lose the ball to the other team
Lost the game no, not us!

*Laura Holt  (9)*
*Hacton JMI School*

## PERSPECTIVES OF AUTUMN

A leaf floats down from the sky,
Golden,
Curled up,
Drifting down,
On a gentle breeze,
To land,
On a carpet full of crispy leaves,
Crunching beneath my feet,
Autumn has come,
But are they really leaves
Falling from the trees?
'Or is it burnt, dried bread?'
The dirty, hungry children said.
I was astonished and it made me think twice,
'Who was right?'
Was it me?
Or was it those hungry children?
Who *could* I ask?
Who *should* I ask?

*Shreedevi Chatterjee (9)*
*Hacton JMI School*


## LIMERICKS

I know a young lad called Paul
He was very, very tall
He couldn't go out
Because he had a big snout
He wished he could be small.

*Alan Manners (9)*
*Hacton JMI School*

## IT'S NOT FAIR

It's not fair
That she gets a CD player.
He gets a ten pound note,
She gets to stay up late,
He gets the TV
It's just not fair.

It's not fair
That she goes in the bath whenever she wants,
He gets the sweets,
She gets her own room
It's just not fair.

It's not fair
He gets the most presents when it's his birthday
And I only get five.
She doesn't clean the windows
So I do
It's just not fair.

*Shane Redford  (9)*
*Hacton JMI School*


## ICY ICICLES

Icy icicles floating from the sky,
Icy icicles drift into my eye.
Icy icicles soaring through the air,
Icy icicles fall into my hair.
Icy icicles cover up my window pane,
Icy icicles can freeze up our water main.

*Jessica Croker  (9)*
*Hacton JMI School*

## A WINDY DAY

On a windy day
the tree leaves
are falling down
on the ground,
floating in the air,
all crunched up.
When the children
are playing
near the tree
the leaves
are crunching
like a crisp.

*Charlene Green  (9)*
*Hacton JMI School*

## BIG SISTER

I have to go to bed early
I have to eat my veg
I have to do something
But I'm not doing what
She says!

She's allowed in the garden
My mum says I'm not
I've got to do something but
I don't know what?

*Steven Nice  (9)*
*Hacton JMI School*

## OPPOSITES

As light as a white piece of paper
floating in the air
As heavy as a ton of bricks
falling on the hard ground
As hot as the boiling sun
turning you brown
As cold as an ice cube
in the freezing fridge
As big as the Eiffel Tower
towering above Paris
As little as a small ant
scattering around the floor
As good as a school child
doing as they are told
As bad as a growling dog
barking and biting
As dry as a rock
hanging on a high cliff
As wet as running water
Washing down the stream.

*Charlotte White (9)*
*Hacton JMI School*


## WINTER'S BLOSSOM

W  hite snowflakes falling to the ground
I   think it's beautiful to see
N  ice and bright as the snow shines out
T  oo cold so animals hibernate
E  verything covered in a glistening blanket of snow
R  obins search for food.

*Christopher Boom (9)*
*Hacton JMI School*

## THE KIPPER AND THE CRAB

I am a fish,
Swimming in the sea,
Hoping that no one catches me,
For if they do I know my fate,
I'll end up on someone's dinner plate.
So Mr Fisherman,
Please be kind,
Catch all the crabs
And leave the fish behind.

I am a crab,
Swimming in the sea,
Everyone seems to catch me.
I wish I could climb on a boat,
I'd say to the skipper,
'Leave the crabs,
And catch the kipper!'

*Jade Warrington (9)*
*Hacton JMI School*

## DANCING

D ance to keep fit
A medal is good to win
N ever give up
C arefully perform new dances
I f you win you should be proud
N ew dances are a challenge
G o and do your best.

*Leigh-Anne Kilcullen (9)*
*Hacton JMI School*

## COSMIC POEM

Shooting stars go over the night
Tonight is calm, the moon still shines
A spaceship flies over the clouds and into the clouds
Rockets shoot into the sky and on the moon
Somewhere over the clouds.

*Cherish Meade (8)*
*Leverton GM Junior School*

## IN SPACE

Stars are white in the sky
Planets orbiting around the sun
Astronaut go up to space
Comets fly in the universe
Earth is big from up above.

*Scott Rodhouse (8)*
*Leverton GM Junior School*

## SPACE POEM

M e and my friends go to space
A  s we enter a dark place
R  otten rocks and floating planets
S  atellites, stars, sun and moon.

*Danielle Bagshaw (8)*
*Leverton GM Junior School*

# UFOs Come Down To Earth

When I go up to bed I open my window
I go to bed I know the sun goes away
And the moon comes to play
UFOs come down to Earth
And fire their guns
And smother the Earth to smithereens.

*Jack Snell (7)*
*Leverton GM Junior School*


# Star Bright Star Light

S  hooting stars in the sky
T  he astronauts fly high high in the sky
A  liens are on Earth
R  ockets fly in the sky
S  tars so bright and so light.

*Ceri Turner (7)*
*Leverton GM Junior School*


# The Shooting Star

S  un and moon
T  he astronauts fire their guns
A  stronauts are on Earth
R  ocks land on Earth
S  hooting stars fly in the sky.

*Stephanie Hilton (7)*
*Leverton GM Junior School*

## MR BOGGLEOW

Space is a place where nothing grows
Space is a place where stars grow
Space is a place where men can't go
Space is a place where no one can go
Until one day a spaceman reached the moon
In an invention called the rocketship
Space is a place now where men can go
Thanks to the man called Mr Boggleow.

*Charlotte Brown (9)*
*Leverton GM Junior School*


## STARS

S hooting rockets in the sky
T elescopes watching out
A liens up so high
R ockets going down
S ee the rockets going down.

*Lakshmi Joshi (7)*
*Leverton GM Junior School*


## SHOOTING STARS

S hooting stars
P eople see
A stronauts far up in the sky
C omets come down to destroy
E arth is the nicest place to go.

*Dale O'Sullivan (7)*
*Leverton GM Junior School*

## SPACE WORLD

C louds above stars below
O ff we fly in the sky
S pacemen on the moon
M en see a shooting star in the sky
I n the spaceship men go
C omets fly in the sky.

*Joanne Page  (8)*
*Leverton GM Junior School*


## SHOOTING STARS

S tars sit quietly in the sky
T elescopes in the sky
A stronauts going into space
R ockets launching
S hooting stars in the sky.

*Anjali Khambhaita  (8)*
*Leverton GM Junior School*


## STARS

S un and moon
T hey both move together
A ll around
R ockets launched
S tars sit in the dark.

*Gemma Cross  (8)*
*Leverton GM Junior School*

## COSMIC POEM

3, 2, 1
Blast off. Up in space. I can't breathe.
Here we go Tom wear a spacesuit.
Thanks that's better.
Look at the shooting star whizzing
through the sky.
Whoosh!
Joanne. Joanne look at the moon.
It is big isn't it. Yes but look at
all the planets.
Mercury, Venus, Earth, Mars, Jupiter,
Saturn, Uranus, Neptune, Pluto.
Quick get ready for it.
Here it comes.
The sun.
It's beautiful.
Oh I wished that dream could
have been real.
Good night.

*Amy McKenzie  (8)*
*Leverton GM Junior School*

## STARS ABOVE

Galaxy is scrummy just right for my tummy
I look out at the stars above,
The stars sit quietly in the night
I find a piece of meteorite.

*Laura Heady  (9)*
*Leverton GM Junior School*

## SWEETS

Sweets are lovely,
Sweets are neat,
Sweets are fun for you to eat,
Sweets are coloured red, green, blue,
There's a lot of things to do.

When you go down to the shops,
Buy your sweets lots and lots.

Get your Mars bars, Polos too,
Bounties, Snickers and raspberry chews.

Last of all sweets are yummy,
But be warned too many
Will hurt your tummy.

*Amy Allen  (8)*
*Nightingale Primary School*




## COME WITH ME

Come with me -
Oh, come and see!
There are blossoms now
On the beechnut tree,
And though the oak tree
Is dark and bare,
A pair of robins
Are nesting there.

*Preeti Sohota  (8)*
*Nightingale Primary School*

# MY PIRATE SHIP

I play a game
Where I'm all at sea
Just me, the cat
And the parrot makes three

I'm the pirate captain
They're the lazy crew
They're a scurvy lot
I have to tell them what to do

I seek desert islands
To find diamonds and gold
Pirate treasures
To fill up the hold

Whatever I do is very bold
In all our fights we are the winners
Our enemies walk the plank
And become shark dinners

It's a hard, hard life
We need our rum
The food is awful
It upsets my tum

We fire our pistols
Both night and day
Sometimes I'm glad
It's only play

Then I tell Mummy
About me and my crew
She thinks we are very brave
To do what we do

The pirate ship is packed away
I'll be back to sail another day.

*Sophie Wise (7)*
*Oaklands School*


## THE SPOOKY NIGHT

The other night, when I was in bed
I heard a noise that went into my head.
I heard it about seven times.
I thought it was a witch, and I cried.
I screamed, and then I called for Mum,
But when I looked, she hadn't come.
I was really really scared.
I tried to go to sleep instead.
Then I heard a knock on the door.
That made me scared even more.
In the morning Mum said
'I knocked on your door again.
You're always screaming dear. Why?
And then you start to cry.'
'Oh, sorry Mum. I thought you were a witch,
But you could have turned on the light switch!'

*Maria Green (8)*
*Oaklands School*

## PONY

There's a pony in my field,
Munching lots of grass,
And some people in the tack room shining up his brass.

There's a pony in my field,
I let him gallop around,
And when he's done he comes back homeward bound.

There's a pony in my field,
His name is Apatche,
And when I show him a carrot,
His mouth turns very snatchy.

There's a pony in my field,
And when the day is done,
I put him in his stable and go and have some fun.

*Natasha Panasiuk  (8)*
*Oaklands School*


## SOPHIA

Sophia is very cute,
She is my baby sister,
Sophia is a little bit chubby,
And she drinks a lot,
And cries a lot,
She looks like me,
She's got my nose, my mouth and toes,
She's got little feet and hands,
She goes to sleep during the day,
But not at night,
So my mummy's very tired.

*Elleni Kyriakides  (7)*
*Oaklands School*

# CREATURES OF THE WORLD

Animals can sometime be very small
Animals are sometimes very tall.
Golden eagles are very big flying across the sky,
When you want to watch them
You've got to look up high.
Gorillas are big and strong
Snakes are slim and long.
Rabbits can hop and run too
Like Skippy the kangaroo.
Spiders are hairy and
Tarantulas are very scary.
Snails are slow and in a shell
Worms are scaly and slow as well.
Dogs have pretty fur
Cats have fluffy fur and purr
Elephants have a nose called a trunk.
There is an animal which is called a skunk.
There is an animal which is big and
brown which is a bear.
There is an animal which is small, grey
which is called a hare.
Baby sheep are called lambs.
Male sheep are called rams.
In Australia there is a dog called a dingo.
In Tenerife there is a bird which is
pink which is called a flamingo.

*Emma Reeves  (8)*
*Oaklands School*

## PARENTS' EVENING

When it comes to parents' evening,
I get a shiver down my spine.
When my teacher called my mum and dad in,
I worry if I get low marks.
While I'm waiting for my parents in the classroom,
I wonder if my behaviour is bad.
I'm thinking if I get nought out of ten in English,
If I do, oh my God! I will be in the lowest group!
My mum and dad say don't worry
You'll get on in the future.
The next morning I don't want to go to school,
When I got to school,
My teacher said I got 10 out of 10 in English.
That afternoon I told my parents,
They said *excellent.*

*Semona Auluk  (8)*
*Oaklands School*


## WHAT'S THAT NOISE UNDER MY BED?

Every night when I go to sleep under my bed I hear this creak,
Is it a cat is it a bat is it a mouse or maybe a rat?
I call for my mum but she doesn't come,
So I call my dad but he's snoring too bad.
I lie in my bed try to hide under the covers down I slide,
I get out of bed have a quick look,
It might be a doll or even a book,
When I put down my head have a quick peek,
It's an old plastic bag that's been making me weak,
I've made all this fuss over a bag,
The mystery solved I'm so glad.

*Gemma Torgut  (8)*
*Oaklands School*

## HALF TERM HOLIDAY

It's half term time
and I've got a week free,
I'm not staying at home
I'm off to ski,
I'm going to Flaine in the Alps in France
I feel so happy I could almost dance,
We drive half way to a town called Troyes
Where we spend the evening playing with our toys,
We started ski school on Sunday morning,
The weather is cold as the day is dawning,
The wind is blowing across my face
It is very cold in this snowy place,
My ski instructor Alex is a very nice man,
I'm going to do the best that I can,
We learn to snow plough, turn and stop
And take a cable car to the top,
A week soon passes and it's time to go
I say goodbye to the mountains and the snow.

*Lauren Jenkin  (8)*
*Oaklands School*


## ACROSTIC POEM

R  abbits can be really fun,
A  ll the people love them,
B  ut sometimes they can jump about,
B  umping all around the house,
I   t is really funny,
T  he tail is really short and
S  ome are really furry and can jump very high.

*Loren O'Connell  (9)*
*St Alban's RC School*

## My Family

My family are kind
My family adore buns
I'll tell you about them
Starting with my mum!

My mum is very helpful
My mum gets a little mad
When Claire and I argue
Now let's get on with my dad.

My dad is very nice
My dad is very fair
My dad fixes all my broken things
Now let's get on with my sister Claire.

My sister Claire is funny
My sister Claire can be silly
I love my sister Claire
Now that's the end of my fam-ily!

*Emily Harrison  (9)*
*St Alban's RC School*


## Football

F  ootball is a very good sport
O  ur class plays
O  verall they are very good
T  actics
B  all control
A  fter play we get a drink
L  ots of people are worn out
L  ots, I mean lots.

*Colin Campbell  (9)*
*St Alban's RC School*

## ACROSTIC POEM

A merica was superb
M y mum was scared on terror tower
E veryone enjoyed it
R eally cool
I got all the characters' autographs
C inderella's castle was bright pink
A nd it was a shame to go home.

*Tom Vargas  (9)*
*St Alban's RC School*


## SPIDERS

S piders are small
P ulling their webs
I n the dark
D oing their stuff
E ating away
R unning from children
S piders are great.

*Harry Tyler  (9)*
*St Alban's RC School*


## DOLPHIN

D olphins are so cute.
O h they are so friendly.
L ovely to play with.
P at them all day.
H ear them every day.
I n the sea I see the dolphin.
N ow it's time to go home.

*Kathleen Gillespie  (9)*
*St Alban's RC School*

## READING

R eading is great, it's also fun,
E verybody and everyone!
A nytime or any place.
D ead scary,
I n the dark.
N obody is frightened or scared,
G oosebumps is the recommended book to read.

*Emma Furzer  (9)*
*St Alban's RC School*


## LITTLE STAR I HEARD YOU CALL ME

It happened a few nights ago,
I heard a little ding ding,
I asked Mum if she heard it
but she said I was dreaming,
I was the only one
in the world who heard it

Next night I heard
someone calling my name
in a light voice
I looked up and heard
the twinkle of a star.

*Abigail Garrard  (8)*
*St Mary's RC JMI School*

## MY MAGIC BOX

I will put in my magic box
A fairy from a magic fantasy.
I will put in my magic box
A lot of wishes.
I would wish for a magic unicorn
from a fantasy.

I will put in my magic box
a whale, a pet dolphin,
a wicked witch, and an angel from heaven.

My magic box is made
from pure gold and silver
with a golden key
to go in a silver keyhole.

I want all these things
because I don't get them in real life
That's why I wish for them.

*Amy Falvey-Browne  (8)*
*St Mary's RC JMI School*


## COMPUTER CRAZY

I love you though you shut down.
I love you though you're silly.
I love you though you can't be found.
I love you though you beep and drive me mad.
I love you though you're very bad.
Yes you're my computer.
Mine Mine
*Mine.*

*Emma Stacey  (8)*
*St Mary's RC JMI School*

## PUZZLE POEM

It looks fierce, it looks sharp
It's ready to eat and it's going to eat fast.
It touches you with its teeth,
It likes you with its teeth,
It takes you to his territory
And it eats you with its teeth.
You can't hear me sometimes
But I creep up behind
And I knock you out with my tail.
It likes to eat seals.
It likes to eat penguins.
It likes to eat humans
And likes to eat someone like you.

*Gregory Hanshaw  (8)*
*St Mary's RC JMI School*

## SIGHT

Sight of my eyes,
What can I see?
Branches blowing here and to me
Again and again I sigh
I see the clock,
It says tick-tock
I walk outside I see a cat
It pounces pounces on me
It pounces on my knee.

*Lianne Shanley  (7)*
*St Mary's RC JMI School*

## THE WIND

The wind is blowing through the trees
through the house and up to me.

Hats flying people crying because
their hats have flown away.

Gates blowing open and shut and
leaves being blown away.

Birds being blown in the sky
and when the wind ends all hats on the floor
and leaves everywhere.

*Francesca Anastasio  (7)*
*St Mary's RC JMI School*


## MY MAGIC BOX

I will put in my magic box
a flying horse
10,000 PlayStation games
A snowman on a broomstick

I will put in my magic box
a chocolate house
a house full of sweets
a chocolate robot

The box is made of gold.

*Jamie Cannell  (8)*
*St Mary's RC JMI School*

## MY MAGIC BOX

I will put in my magic box
an ocean with a squid
and a Loch Ness
and it will be the biggest ocean
in the world.
I will put in my magic box
sharks and a blue whale.
but my box will still have
room to fit a three-eyed fish.
My magic box is made of seaweed
on the side and sharks' teeth for the corners
and fish eyes for the top and the bottom.
I will swim around and
touch the animals with my fingertips
and they will be friendly to me
and I'll do that every day.

*Keiran Lloyd Jones  (7)*
*St Mary's RC JMI School*


## THE BEDTRAIN

When I lie in bed in the
middle of the night,
When there's never a soul in sight,
I hear the ch, ch of a train,
and I'm sure it's not the sound of rain.
The train is running through the room,
It sounds like the trucks
you find in a tomb.

*Liam Cox  (7)*
*St Mary's RC JMI School*

# TASTE

I like your taste you're round and in
the middle you've got bumps
My best flavour is salt and vinegar
When I put you in my mouth you crackle
When I crunch you up so you see
What do you think, have you guessed?
It's crisps, do you like crisps?
Because I do as you can see in this poem.

*Alexander Miller  (7)*
*St Mary's RC JMI School*

# PUZZLE POEM

*Look* it's as fast as a snowflake.
*Touch* it's as hard as a piece of metal.
*Sound* it makes a noise like the fastest racing car.
*Smell* it leaves behind a smell of petrol and fire.

*Luke Sampayo  (7)*
*St Mary's RC JMI School*

# MY TEDDY

I love you though you have no hair.
I love you though your stuffing has come out.
I love you though your arm has fell off.
I love you though your leg has come out.

*Warren James  (7)*
*St Mary's RC JMI School*

## MAGIC BOX

In my magic box I will put
A flying horse with wings so delicate,
Lots of beautiful violets,
A magical crown with lots of beautiful jewels
A giant seahorse you can ride on
with some lovely reins.

I will also put sheets and sheets of silk
That carry you where you want,
Three or four wishes all of my choice,
A coconut tree with juice so milky,
A palace decorated with such imagination
and such pretty colours and such royalty.

A magical hat that produces rabbits - fancy that.
A pouch full of jewellery that is so pretty
and the pouch made of velvet,
A wonderful country mansion,
A chest of gold.

A lovely hot country,
A luxury ship that will not break,
A log ride from a theme park,
A giant chocolate bar,
My magic box is made of jewels and a golden lid
A wish on each corner and a secret each side.

*Jessica Dodd  (7)*
*St Mary's RC JMI School*

## SHOOTING STARS

At night they fly
across the moon
Far away
they zoom and zoom
they are like little rockets
in the air
setting off to space
but where oh where?
probably going to see aliens
or go to fly to another planet
shooting stars may look so small
but shooting stars
are pretty tall
they go so fast across the stars
over houses they zoom so far.

*Jamie Jones  (8)*
*St Mary's RC JMI School*


## SIGHT

I can see . . .
I can see the shadow of a ghost!
I can see Australia
I can see inside your body
I can see another galaxy
I can see vibration
I can see a blind man's sight!
I can see the past!
I can see a dead man's life!
I can see almost everything!

*Christopher Hawkins  (8)*
*St Mary's RC JMI School*

## SOUNDS I HEAR IN MY HOUSE

Creak creak goes the stairs.
Tick tock goes the clock by night.
Broom broom the cars go by.
Glitter glitter the lamps shiver.
Bring bring *Ahhhh!* goes the clock by night.

*Joseph Campbell-Briggs  (8)*
*St Mary's RC JMI School*


## SOUND

I hear video but I don't know who's watching it
I hear somebody calling my name
But now I look out an owl is calling my name,
I hear birds singing in the trees
Owls hooting in the trees.

*Claire Mersh  (7)*
*St Mary's RC JMI School*


## SUN

You shine in the sky
I can see you fly by
You would never fade away
So OK you can stay
Sun sun how high in the sky
Above all the people but night night bye bye.

*Liam McDowell  (9)*
*St Mary's RC JMI School*

## MR MOON

Aliens plunder,
Asteroids blunder,
But what does Mr Moon do?
He shines all night and he shines with light,
He's far away in flight,
Jupiter's cold,
Mars is bold,
But nothing's better than Mr Moon,
He moons and shoons without a doubt,
Like an astronaut clowning about,
But now I've heard each planet has a moon,
I don't know which one plays my tune.

*Robert Gadie  (9)*
*St Mary's RC JMI School*

## GARDEN AT AUTUMN

When it is autumn
I go in my garden
and all the colours
in the trees fall off.
The conkers fall off
and I collect conkers to play .
When it is autumn
The wind blows hard.
All different things fall off.

*Omer Kekin  (8)*
*St Mary's RC JMI School*

## THE TOGETS

I'm going in a zooming rocket,
I brought some things in my pocket
for my friends the Togets.
Togets are nasty,
Togets are bad,
Togets make me feel
rather sad.

They live in a planet
called Holmer,
The Togets are as
large as a boulder,
So when they go to pick me up,
They put me down with a tut.

Uh oh here one comes
Sticking out his tongue,
I think I'd better run
This isn't fun.

*Joshua Adamson  (9)*
*St Mary's RC JMI School*


## SOUND

I can hear the air
But no one else can.
The air floats in the sky.
The air floats everywhere
And it even floats in my house.

*Jack Morrison  (7)*
*St Mary's RC JMI School*

## STARS

Stars twinkle in the sky
Like little lights that come on at night
I watch them shoot across the sky
They lay in space
Looking down at me
The stars glow in the sky
The sun comes up they go to bed
Wanting the sun to go down
So they can show their light again
That is what stars do over night.

*Aimee Warr  (8)*
*St Mary's RC JMI School*

## A METEOR JUST CRASHED HERE

I'm going to Mars
For a cup of tea
With my best friend ET.
Then off I go
To planet Mo
To find a frog's big warty toe.
Then after that
I heard a splat
A meteor has just crashed flat
Oh dear! Oh dear!

*Elliott Davis  (8)*
*St Mary's RC JMI School*

## ALIENS WHY DON'T YOU GO HOME?

Aliens why don't you go home?
Aliens why don't you invade Rome?
Stop bothering me you troublesome three.
Please! Stop bothering me.

You can stay with me if you like,
But don't jump up and fight.
Please stop bothering me.
You said you're going to tea.
I'm glad you didn't stay.
Please go away.
I'm glad you didn't stay.
Goodbye for another day.

*Ursula Long  (9)*
*St Mary's RC JMI School*


## MILKY WAY AND MARS

Milky Way and Mars,
These are chocolate bars.
Are the aliens peckish?
Hungry for their fetish.
I want to go to the moon
In a rocket that can zoom.
I'll see the aliens go *Ho Ho Ho*
And maybe some UFOs.
But most of all I want to see
If there are chocolate bars for me.

*Jayne Wood  (8)*
*St Mary's RC JMI School*

## PLANET TO PLANET

Rockets go zooming way up high
To see the stars in the sky.
Then on to the Milky Way they go
To drink the milk with a yo ho ho.

Then off for a piece of cheese
From the moon.
There they say a big hello to the moon people
They're friendly folk you know.

Then on to Mars for a cup of tea
With the aliens as big as me.
Of course you know in the galaxy
The Milky Way and on Mars
You may find a lot of chocolate bars.

Next they go to Saturn and back
The spacemen better hold onto their hats.
There they find a smelly cat
And kick it out with a rat-a-tat-tat.

Now it's time to say goodbye
To all the creatures in the sky
So home they go with a glow.

*Rachel Denham (9)*
*St Mary's RC JMI School*


## I LOVE YOU BECAUSE . . .

I love you because you are cuddly,
I love you because your little eyes gleam at me.
I love you because you squeak at dinner time.
I love you because you are my guinea-pigs.

*Tessa Doughty (7)*
*St Mary's RC JMI School*

## Wish I Was You

I'm a dull boring asteroid
Floating through space
Suddenly a flicker goes across my face
A glorious thing indeed
Love to be that, I plead
As I move on, my face gets dull
Like a smelly sock in a rotten bowl
I came across an alien
Purple and spotted
Not like me I've already rotted
I've just figured out
I must have the flu.

*Kieren Browne (9)*
*St Mary's RC JMI School*


## Smells

I like the smell of flowers especially the rose,
I like the smell of soap,
I love it when it slips in your hand.
I like the smell of the dog when it's clean,
I like the smell of aftershave.

*Matthew Mundy (8)*
*St Mary's RC JMI School*

## THE DAZZLING COMET

Wow, wo, yippee, what a ride.
It's round. It's fat
It's like the top of a tennis bat.
Back and forth all the time
Making the day go past so fine.
It's a ball of fire whizzing
through space and its destination
is a far off place.
With several little friends
that whiz through space too,
They zoom about impressing
me and you.
Comets dazzle through the night sky
Showing off how well they can fly.
The comet's reign ends when the sun appears
Causing the beautiful comet to disappear.

*Billy Hollyfield (9)*
*St Mary's RC JMI School*


## A BLACK NIGHT

Spacemen floating in the sky
Shooting stars in a black night
And a silver moon
Mars, Jupiter and Pluto
Oh I wish I was on the moon
Oh isn't it fun,
Seeing zooming rockets on the run,
I do wish I was on the moon.

*Katie Murphy (8)*
*St Mary's RC JMI School*

## SPACE

I'd love to visit space one day,
But I don't think my parents would say 'OK'
Visit the planets all around,
Lots of planets to be found.
Lots of rockets in the sky,
Shooting stars passing by,
All the planets have lovely patterns
Jupiter, Venus, Mars and Saturn.
My favourite one is the Earth
And that is where I had my birth.

*Jack Nash  (9)*
*St Mary's RC JMI School*


## SHOOTING STARS

One day I went
up to the moon.
I hope I get
there very soon.
To see shooting stars
and on to Mars.
I never knew
it was so dark in space.
I don't think it's the place
for the human race.

*Yasmin Lowe  (8)*
*St Mary's RC JMI School*

## FLOATING IN SPACE

I'm floating in space,
Having so much fun,
I've seen lots of planets,
As well as the sun.

I've met an alien,
He's weird and strange,
But cool and funky,
Top of the range.

I've met some friends,
They're called Bib and Bob,
They're hairy and smelly,
A couple of slobs.

Come to space,
It's full of stars,
One's called Jupiter,
One's called Mars.

We've been to the sun,
The stars and the moon,
We really can't wait,
Till I come back soon.

*Kayleigh Brown  (9)*
*St Mary's RC JMI School*

## EXPLORING SPACE

Zooming through the sky
On my way to the moon
It's going to take a while
I won't be there soon
Everything below is looking small
In a flash you can't see them at all
Flying through the clouds
Like a shooting star
To the moon it is very far
As the rocket ship blasts into the night
I can't see the cloud because it is no longer light
Floating around in the silvery space
On my way to the moon there is no time to waste
What will I find when I get there
Big green monsters with golden hair
Two-headed monkeys and talking dogs
Flying horses and giant green frogs
A friendly tiger I might meet
Wearing a bow tie and boots on his feet
Zooming through the sky on my way to the moon
It won't take long I'll be there soon.

*Nicholas Tyler (9)*
*St Mary's RC JMI School*


## THE SEA AND WIND

I must go down to the sea again
When the wind is high and rushing by
When the waves are spinning ships up high
When the waves are strong and the clouds are grey
Blowing, blowing ships away.

*Christopher Benney (8)*
*St Mary's RC JMI School*

## THE FRIENDLY ALIENS

Aliens aliens come to me,
I'm friendly and there's no one with me,
Here they are coming to me,
Very slimy, spotty and hairy I can see,

Aliens speak to me,
I don't know where Earth is can you help me?
Yes yes it's right over there,
I don't have a spaceship,
You can have that one over there,
Thank you thank you,
You are so kind,
How can I thank,
Well goodbye.

*Lee Summerfield  (9)*
*St Mary's RC JMI School*


## ALIENS IN MARS

They're funky
They're furry
They're monsters tonight
They stink of broccoli
They're green, black and white
They're very ugly
They haven't seen a moon buggy
If they had they would have to hurry
They're stuffing human munches
In their tummy.

*Andrew Shaw  (9)*
*St Mary's RC JMI School*

## PLANETS

Mercury is small
It's as small as a ping pong ball
Venus is hot
It's so hot you could cook a pottery pot

Mars is red
As red as my friend Fred
Jupiter is made of liquid
And is not solid to land on

Saturn is beautiful
Because of its rings
Uranus is the planet
That spins on its side

Neptune has a great dark spot
It's even fifty times bigger than a dot
Pluto is the smallest planet
At night it is ten times colder than a freezer.

*Kathryn Southgate  (9)*
*St Mary's RC JMI School*


## WIND

W ild, whirling, whispering winds.
 I  n and out, high and low, twirling, swirling
      as they go.
N  orth wind chilling my bones, chattering my teeth
      and freezing me so.
D  aytime, night-time anytime at all,
      The winds decide when they want to call.

*Fransesca Keogh  (8)*
*St Mary's RC JMI School*

## THE MOON IN SPACE

The moon can be found
It's miles around,
It comes out at night
It is so so bright.
The spacemen fly their rockets,
but can't even find their pockets.
They look to the ground
but nobody's found,
all night long
far far around.
There are strange creatures
without a care,
and nobody can see them anywhere.
*What can they be?*

**Samantha Manuel  (9)**
**St Mary's RC JMI School**


## WIND

Whistling wind blowing through the night,
Making the rubbish bins blow over
and giving me a fright.
Trees swaying and leaves falling down,
Rustling and crunching the leaves that are brown.
Swirling and racing past my window,
Making the rivers cold and flowers blow.
It seems to be gentle, sometimes rough,
I'm glad I am indoors the wind can be tough!

**Abbie Richardson  (7)**
**St Mary's RC JMI School**

## THE WIND

Read this poem and you will see
how very different the wind can be

Branches swaying in a gentle breeze
cause autumn leaves to fall from trees
while lines of washing slowly dry
kites and gliders fly up high

Gale-force winds are very strong
the list of damage is often long
the sea gets rough, ports are shut
and back on land we have power cuts

Aeroplanes cannot come or go
until such winds no longer blow.

*Verity Whiter  (7)*
*St Mary's RC JMI School*


## A SEEING POEM

The first time I saw the world
I was glad I had been born
For I saw my mum and dad
I like to see the water
Crashing against the rocks
I like to see the butterflies fluttering around
I like the busy bees the flowers as well.

*Michael Carter  (8)*
*St Mary's RC JMI School*

## COSMIC

A weird creature I saw.
He had four eyes.
Two noses and one mouth.
His eyes were shining like stars.
Luckily we were on Mars.
The creature was dark and slimy
and it came closer.
It started walking and talking.
He said 'Do you want to come
round to my house?'
I did not dare.
He pulled me to the door of his slimy house.
I had slime on my hands
from where he touched me.
He said 'You are from Earth,'
He took me in his house,
Showed me his family and friends.
I'm tired I'm going to bed
You can go now back to Earth.

*Lisa Forbes (9)*
*St Mary's RC JMI School*


## THE WIND

The wind whistles through the trees.
It goes by tree by tree.
The wind is invisible.
In the wood the branches wave.
The wind makes the leaves swirl
Making patterns on the ground.

*Katy Coombs (8)*
*St Mary's RC JMI School*

## ALIEN'S VISIT TO EARTH

Red alert, red alert,
Or is it green alert?
Everyone shouts
As they spot a funky, funny
Extraterrestrial.

Will it be dangerous, will it be mean?
Or will it be exactly like me?
Here it comes, here it comes,
Burning through the atmosphere.
Here it comes, here it comes
Then it just disappears!
Where it lies we do not know,
But it's long gone now!
Is it blue or is it brown?
Why try to find out?
It's long gone now!

*Matthew Shaw  (9)*
*St Mary's RC JMI School*


## SOUND

I love the sound of birds singing.
I love the sound of babies giggling
and the sound of the wind.
I love the sound of the sea
and the sound of pancakes sizzling.
I love the sound of trees rustling
and Mum and Dad laughing.

*Nuala Duffy  (7)*
*St Mary's RC JMI School*

## WILL THEY DIE?

Comets zooming,
saucers spinning,
dodging in and out.
Still pursuing,
gaining speed,
through some weed and out of a spout.
'Missed!' some cry,
while the comet flies,
But the question is,
Will they die?
Just a moment later,
*Smash!* It went with a crash.
I know what you are thinking,
where did it crash?
There's no sign anywhere,
But I don't really care.

*Robert Hough  (9)*
*St Mary's RC JMI School*


## SIGHTS IN KOS

I love to see the sun go down at night
I love the sight of two ships closing in the sea
I love the view from a high restaurant
Looking down to the town
I love the sight of the waves crashing on the rocks
I love to see butterflies fluttering by.

*Michael Ramkin  (7)*
*St Mary's RC JMI School*

## AN ASTRONAUT LOST ON MARS

'I'm lost, I'm lost in outer space
I don't know where but I'm somewhere
I can see something and it's over there!
It's big and fat and ugly too.
*Aaaarrrggghhh!* It's a family of aliens,' he said.
There're red, blue, yellow and green ones
big, small, large and wide.
They all have four heads, three legs and eyes too.
He said 'I'm lost, where am I?'
The aliens replied, 'You are on Mars.'
The astronaut was scared to bits
the slimy, stinky and smelly things
were coming towards him and trying to kill
He jumped into the spacecraft as quickly as could be
He zoomed away faster and faster
and soon he was home again.

*Lauren Pereira  (9)*
*St Mary's RC JMI School*

## SOUNDS

I love the sound of birds singing
And the sounds of people cheering,
I love the sound of cats in the night,
And the sound of the wind blowing a kite.
I love the sound of the sea
And the sound of people whistling for me.

*William Walsh  (7)*
*St Mary's RC JMI School*

## THE WIND

The wind can be gentle
The wind can be strong
A breeze on my face
Or push me along.

The south wind is warm
The north wind is cold
In hurricanes it whips up trees
It's fearless and bold.

Rush rush rushing by
It never seems to stop
It blows so cold in my face
And makes my ears go pop!

*Billy Ringwood  (8)*
*St Mary's RC JMI School*


## SIGHT

I like to see the sun
rising in the morning.
It shines into my kitchen
nearly every day.
It is so yellow and bright
and in the day it is fully out.
The sun is happy it makes me feel
like going out to play,
it makes me feel hot and cosy.

*Liam McEvoy  (8)*
*St Mary's RC JMI School*

## THE WIND

When you're walking down the street
And your hair is very neat,
The wind comes whistling round the bend
And suddenly your hair's on end.

One day there was a little breeze,
And it came blowing through the trees.
The leaves fell off onto the ground,
And they were swirling round and round.

A strong, cold wind that makes you shiver,
And all over you tingle and quiver.
You hold your coat around you tight,
And walk and walk with all your might.

When you know there is a gale,
Ships find it hard to sail.
Boats come rolling over the sea;
Watch them all - one, two, three.

The wind it moans - it moans and sighs;
It comes and goes and sometimes dies.
I like the sounds - the sounds it makes
As it crosses seas and lakes.

I hate the storm - it makes a noise;
I must stay in and play with toys.
There's lightning sometimes; thunder too.
I'd rather stay here and talk to you.

Goodbye, goodbye, I have to go,
Because the wind is bringing snow.
I'll see you in the summertime,
I hope you liked my little rhyme.

*Anna Van Haeften  (8)*
*St Mary's RC JMI School*

## OH NO! WHAT A WINDY DAY!

Umbrellas turning upside down
leaves turning round and round.
People's hats blowing away
Oh no! What a windy day!

The sky turns dark
no children play in the park
People's washing flying away.
Oh no! What a windy day!

The wind whistles and blows,
it picks up dust and round it goes.
Wind, oh wind please go away
Oh no! What a windy day!

*Sophie McGuire (8)*
*St Mary's RC JMI School*




## SEEING

I love to see fireworks and I
Like to see it snowing down on me.
I like to see birds flying in the air
and I like to see flowers growing.
I like to see new babies.
I love to see the sea whooshing
up the beach and I love to see
the leaves blowing in the wind.

*Joe Staunton (8)*
*St Mary's RC JMI School*

## THE CONSTELLATIONS

Up in the sky when the stars align
they make many constellations.
While Taurus, Leo and Ursa Major battle with fear
to do this the skies must be clear.
Then Scorpio appears.
You can see them through your telescope in the galaxies.
Here comes Sagittarius to battle with Scorpio,
Sagittarius wins and leaves him to woe.
Pisces swims through the dark blue sky
and Cygnus the swan swims with it.
Then with the bright of day, they just seem to go away.

*David Nefs  (9)*
*St Mary's RC JMI School*


## THE WIND

The wind is invisible as it moves the trees.
It pushes boats in the high seas.
There's a breeze on my face, as it whistles past
It's coming from the north,
I can't walk very fast,
Now the wind is blowing a gale
I am going indoors before the hail.

*Santi O'Regan  (7)*
*St Mary's RC JMI School*

## THE WIND

The wind is rushing through the trees
gently blowing in the breeze.
Hear it whistle like a train
rushing forcefully in the rain.
Cold as snow, the north wind blows
gusting strongly around my toes.
Sighing in the windy road
like a sleeping, musty toad.
Oh the wind, invisible and clear,
Watch out a storm is coming near.

*Lucy-Rae Monnoyer (7)*
*St Mary's RC JMI School*


## I LIKE THE TOUCH ...

I like the touch of sand because
it is smooth and tickly.
I like the touch of a football
bouncing on my foot
I like the touch of money
because it is cold and smooth
I like to squeeze a ball
and be tickled by a feather.

*Kevin Balding (8)*
*St Mary's RC JMI School*

## THE WIND

I am the wind, forceful and strong.
You can't see me, but I'll blow you along.
Sometimes a gale and sometimes a breeze.
You will find me on land and across the seas.

Blowing and gushing with plenty of rain.
Bang goes the door again and again.
But I am not all bad I am sure you will agree.
Because if something needs drying I'll do it for free.

*Kirsty Harding  (8)*
*St Mary's RC JMI School*

## THE WIND

The invisible wind is floating by,
Nice and gentle from the sky.
Windy days are often cold,
so rushing by are the old,
The wind is sighing blowing the trees,
whatever happened to that gentle breeze?
It doesn't look safe as the wind gets strong
A few moments ago it was whistling a song,
so forceful it is now gusting along.
When I woke up there was nothing going on.

*Alex Ievoli  (8)*
*St Mary's RC JMI School*

## THE WIND

The wind is blowing
the sea is whirling
flicking water in the air.

The wind is blowing
the sails are rattling
the boats are sailing away.

The wind is blowing
the trees are rustling
the leaves go up in the air.

*Anthony Cable  (7)*
*St Mary's RC JMI School*




## WINDY DAYS

The wind is fast on a stormy day,
rushing around in each different way.
It whispers to you as you go out,
the wind goes out and about.
You can hear but not see him,
as he whistles by deep and thin.
As you feel the breeze on your face,
let the wind go and let the wind race.

*Janice Crafer  (8)*
*St Mary's RC JMI School*

## THE MOON

The moon is round,
it's easily found,
it sparkles at night,
and is very bright,
it is like a light,
it shines at night,
it is colourful and bright.
I'd like to go to the moon one night.
I'd tell all my friends back at school
and talk about it in the hall.

*Kieron Mahoney  (9)*
*St Mary's RC JMI School*


## SOUND

I like the sound of whistling
and the sound of birds
The sound of the sea and
the buzzing of bees.
Water gushing from the taps
and the trees rustling.
I like the sound of the
brakes when the bus stops.

*Adam Summers  (8)*
*St Mary's RC JMI School*

## MAN'S FIRST STEP AND MEETING ALIENS

Man's first step
was a great big step
Straight down onto the moon.
Looking around I saw craters and no water.
It was amazing!
But at first it was very mysterious
because it was silent
and nothing was moving.
No gravity upon it.
Then I saw a flash go by
and then the flash stopped and looked at me.
It was such an ugly sight
with four big eyes.
They winked and blinked at me.
I thought this was strange.
There is no life on the moon!
When it stopped winking and blinking
I got a better look,
A blue body with yellow spots
a purple head, green furry hair.
It came close to me
and I began to run
back to the space shuttle
and straight back to Earth
to tell my great finding
to the whole of the Earth.

*Patrick How  (9)*
*St Mary's RC JMI School*

## ALIENS ON THE MOON

One day in outer space
I saw an alien with an ugly face
He had two eyes and two heads
He had six tentacles and two legs
He had razor teeth and
not to mention that revolting smell.
And then I saw on both sides
About 156 million of them, I guess
But I knew there were no aliens on the moon
But then I realised
It was only Neil Armstrong
I landed on the moon
And opened the door
and saw 156 million aliens.
I gasped. Then I dashed back inside
but a tentacle grabbed me
And pulled me outside again.
They looked at me with a hungry look.
I wriggled and turned from side to side
But I still could not get free
from those ugly beasts.
But then I saw from out of the sky
a meteor as big as the team
*Splat!*
I flew back to where I had started
and went back to bed
after a hard day's work.

*Jonathan Smith  (9)*
*St Mary's RC JMI School*

## SPACE AND THE UNIVERSE

An exciting journey will be made,
by the most experienced grade.
The journey will be taken,
by a group of men,
7, 8, 9, maybe ten!
They'll reach the moon in time for tea.
There'll also be no gravity.
Ahead of them they will see,
a weird and wonderful galaxy.
The astronauts see funny creatures
with some strange funny features.
They'll suck some blood out of your feet,
eat your flesh and think it's meat.
They're ugly snarling beasts so tall,
trip them over and they will fall.
The captain calls 'Let's get out of here!
Let's leave this horrible atmosphere.
Down to Earth we will come,
our mission's nearly done.'
When we land I'll be out,
run, run, run, shout, shout, shout.
I'll never ever go up again
and never ever feel the pain.

*Dominic Cox  (10)*
*St Mary's RC JMI School*

## SMELLS

When I am in the swimming pool
I smell chlorine.
When I am out in the garden
I smell flowers.
My favourite one is a rose.
When my mum is cooking
I like the smell.

*Stuart Manuel  (8)*
*St Mary's RC JMI School*


## THE WIND

As I sit here looking out I can
hear the wind howling about
wind howling up the street
picking me up off
my feet.

*Danielle Edwards  (7)*
*St Mary's RC JMI School*


## SOUND

I love the sound of birds singing,
water gurgling in the sink.
Listening to my favourite music,
my dad whistling when he's walking,
and the rain plopping in puddles.

*Christopher More  (7)*
*St Mary's RC JMI School*

## MY POEM

I love the sun setting
because of the lovely colours it makes.
Blue, green, red and orange.
But most of all I love the stars
that come out at night.
They twinkle and shine in the black sky.

*Sean Freeman  (7)*
*St Mary's RC JMI School*


## PUZZLE POEM

It is fiery with a bit of smoke and light.
You can touch it,
And it is as smooth as a dolphin's skin.
It sounds like a bomb blowing up.
It smells of burning rubber.

*A rocket.*

*Georgina McAusland*
*St Mary's RC JMI School*


## SOUND

I can hear the owl calling my name
but no one is calling my name.
I can hear music coming from the stars.
They are twinkling very nicely.
I like the sounds of the stars twinkling.

*Laura Attwaters  (7)*
*St Mary's RC JMI School*

## SPACE

Zooming rockets fill the air
Shooting stars give me a scare
I wonder if aliens will let me
go up there.

Maybe they will
Maybe they won't
I'd love to go into space
And see their face
When I say I want to play chase.

*Jodie Murphy (8)*
*St Mary's RC JMI School*


## A SEA HAS SALT

A sea has salt but has no chips,
A bone has a body, but has no dogs,
Flour has eggs, but has no petals,
Tables have chairs but have no numbers,
A watch is a watch though it cannot see.

*Alice Macris (8)*
*St Mary's RC JMI School*


## LISTENING

I love the sound of
music playing.
The wind whistling,
stars twinkling,
and cats purring.

*Jordan Grainger (7)*
*St Mary's RC JMI School*

## MRS MOON

I see it in the sky
It comes at night
It is so bright
It is called the moon
It plays a tune.

There's water on the moon
It shines so very bright.

Stars go to Mars
Look out for flying bars.

*Teresa Willis (9)*
*St Mary's RC JMI School*

## THE EGGS ARE HATCHING

Spring is coming, hens are laying
Lambs are playing, rolling in the grass.
All the birds are singing and the rabbits are out bouncing.
Lots of kids are happy and eating chocolate.

*Joshua Dines (9)*
*Springfield PNEU School*

## BUTTERFLIES

Butterflies are beautiful,
Butterflies are bright.
Butterflies are colourful,
Butterflies are light.

Butterflies are blue,
Butterflies are orange too.
Butterflies are yellow and green,
Butterflies are sometimes cream.

There are large
And small
Big and all,
Everywhere!

Butterflies are spring,
Butterflies make me sing.
Butterflies are in me and you
I like butterflies, do you?

*Rosalind Mearns  (9)*
*Springfield PNEU School*

# DO THIS, DO THAT

My mum said 'Tidy your room.'
My mum said 'Wash the car.'
I get fed up with her saying do this,
I wish I could do it to her.

My dad said 'Don't be rude.'
My dad said 'Don't go outside.'
All I want to do is play football,
I wish I had a place to hide.

Laura said 'Feed the cats.'
Laura said 'Be quiet.'
It annoys me when she shouts at me
It causes such a riot.

Jess said 'Give me my football.'
Jess said 'Let's have a fight.'
I hate it when everyone shouts at me
Especially when I am right.

The cats don't shout - they love me
I love them too
When I am upset
My mum gives me a cuddle -*Phew!*

When I have won a race
Jessie plays with me
Then everyone is happy
I love my family.

*Alex Sorrell (9)*
*Springfield PNEU School*

## PETS

I want a pet, anything will do.
A dog,
a cat,
a rabbit,
a hamster,
Just give me one please.
A guinea-pig,
a gerbil,
a mouse,
a parrot,
you can share it too.
A pony,
a horse,
a donkey,
a tortoise.
I'm begging you on my knees.
Pleee . . . ase.

*Katie Jayne Hall (9)*
*Springfield PNEU School*


## DARK

Dark, dark,
I am scared of the dark,
As I walk in the night
Looking for nasty people.

Dark, dark,
Nobody can see me in the dark,
People do not like the dark,
It is very dark outside.

*Donna Cracknell (8)*
*Thames View Junior School*

## HOLIDAYS

Holidays, holidays
hot sweaty holidays,
going to the zoo
and never having fun.

Holidays, holidays
hot sweating holidays,
As I walk to the sea
eating my lollipop.

Holidays, holidays
hot, sweating holidays
playing in the sand
splashing in the sea.

*Amy Stone  (8)*
*Thames View Junior School*


## THIS IS THE LEG

This is the leg
that helps me to walk
that gets me out of bed
that takes me to school.

This is the leg
that helped me to walk
that got me out of bed
that took me to school.
This is the leg that
takes me about.

*Michael Kemp  (8)*
*Thames View Junior School*

## THE CAT

His eyes are stars at night
His paws are like leather
His hiss is like a gust of wind
The cat hunts for his prey
His ears are as stiff as a match.

*Tom Manning  (9)*
*Thames View Junior School*


## THE CAT

His teeth are as sharp as a dagger
His breath smells like a winter's morning
His tail is as long as a rattlesnake
The cat's acorn eyes are large and round
His colour is as dark as the night sky.

*Anthony Spurr Jr  (9)*
*Thames View Junior School*


## THE CAT

Her eyes are as blue as the bluest sea
Her sounds are like a purring engine
Her paws are like velvet
The cat hunts for food
Her claws are as sharp as a dagger.

*Rachel Wheeler  (9)*
*Thames View Junior School*

# THIS IS THE FOOT

This is the foot
that helps me walk
that's attached to my leg
that guides me to bed.

This is the foot
that kicks the ball
that scores the goals
rattling the net
that makes me win.

This is the foot
that walks me to school
in the morning time
and starts at nine.

This is the foot
that takes me home
at five past three
to have my tea.

This is the foot
that took me home
that walked me to school
that kicked the ball
that helped me walk
this is the foot
that's steady like rock.

*Jade Trowbridge (9)*
*Thames View Junior School*

## THE WOOLLY MAMMOTH

The woolly mammoth
Fur as warm as the sun
Big long tusks
Frightening everyone
Cold, cold is the world outside
The woolly mammoth all warm inside
Too bad for the woolly mammoth
By this time they're extinct
All the bones sink
Into quicksand
For archaeologists to find.

*Dhanya Pratheep  (8)*
*Thames View Junior School*


## THE CAT

Her fur is as soft as my pillow,
Her eyes are like footballs,
Her teeth are like thousands of forks,
The cat hunts at night in the moonlight
Her claws are as sharp as a knife.

*Deborah Stevens  (9)*
*Thames View Junior School*


## DARK DARK

The streetlights are on
Shining like the sun brightly
Can't see anything.

*Frankie Robinson  (8)*
*Thames View Junior School*

## COLOURS

Red is a devil
Black means Cheryl
Yellow is light
Orange is bright
Pink is heaven
Blue is like seven
Green is a pea
Brown is like tea
Purple is dark
Dark green is a park.

*Stella Arenillas  (9)*
*Thames View Junior School*


## THE CAT

Her steps are slow like a bird.
Her eyes are like eyes shining.
Her fur is as soft as silk.
The cat goes and hunts in the woods.
Her claws are as sharp as a knife.

*Nikki Tolley  (9)*
*Thames View Junior School*


## VOLCANO

Volcano moving
Lava bursting, rocks bouncing
crashing to the floor.

*Jay Kristiansen  (9)*
*Thames View Junior School*

# PIG

Pig
Pink, snorting,
Silky, smelly, muddy
Rolling in the mud
Slow.

*Luke Veazey (8)*
*Thames View Junior School*


# DOG

Dog
Barking, sniffing,
Playing, digging, scratching,
Hunting mice in gardens
Sleeping.

*Matthew Webb (9)*
*Thames View Junior School*


# CAT

Cat
Prowling, rolling,
wandering, running, chasing
Missed that tired mouse
running.

*Connie Taylor (9)*
*Thames View Junior School*

## MISHA COLEEN TRUMPET

M  is for mouse, it runs very fast.
I   is for insects, some fly, some don't.
S   is for sandwich, you can have some butter in it.
H  is for house, you live in it.
A  is for apple, it is round and red.

C  is for cake, it is lovely to eat
O  is for orange, it is round and juicy
L  is for ladybird, it is red and black
E  is for elephant, grey and heavy
E  is for Emma, she is my friend.
N  is for nest, birds lay their eggs in it.

T  is for teddy, all brown and furry
R  is for rainbow, all different colours
U  is for umbrella, it keeps you dry when it is raining.
M  is for moon, it shines in the night.
P  is for parrot, all colourful and bright.
E  is for English, you speak it
T  is for TV, you watch it all day.

*Misha Trumpet  (9)*
*Thames View Junior School*


## SEA AND SAND

Soft as fur is sand
Sea splashing, flowing over
Calmly lays the sand.

*Katie Byrne  (9)*
*Thames View Junior School*

## My Mum

My mum is loud
She scares people away
They won't come back
Until the next day
My mum's like a big bear
But she hasn't much hair.

*Daniel Jones  (8)*
*Thames View Junior School*

## Dog

Dog,
Snarling, growling,
Biting, barking, bounding,
He's catching a robber!
Prowling.

*Patrick Kenny  (8)*
*Thames View Junior School*

## Fear

Fear, trembling at dark
hedgehogs appearing in bushes.
When I go to bed my heart pounds
the bedroom becomes gloomy.

*Daniel Binder  (9)*
*Thames View Junior School*

## THE BLACK CAT

The black cat scampers
through the trees
as the night turns dark.
Down the alley-way the wind
blows fast *woooooooo!*
*Miiiaaaooowww!*
*Crash!*
*Bang!*
*Wallop!*
A car hits the cat
Poor cat!
A few days later
only one life lost
down the alley-way.
Every night and every day
the cat is happy to play.

*Lucy May Guest  (8)*
*Thames View Junior School*

## DOG

Dog
biting, scratching
eating, running, mad
chewing his bone
delicious!

*Josiah Oyekunle  (8)*
*Thames View Junior School*

## THE MISSING CAT

'Pussy, Pussy!' Where's my cat?
Is he under the hat?
Is he under the mat?
'Pussy, Pussy!' Where is he?
Maybe he is looking for me.
I asked my mum who was making the tea.
'Have you seen my cat?'
'Have you looked under the hat
Or under the mat?'
'Yes!'
'No.'
I asked Tim.
Guess who is on the bed?
It is my cat, Fred.

*Joe Cunningham  (8)*
*Thames View Junior School*


## IN THE NIGHT

Wicked old witch
In a big, big, castle.
The wind is blowing fast all night.
Rain, rain crashing in the night.
*Miaow, Miaow,*
The witch's cat squeals.
So scary at night
No candle at night.
The bat in the night
Flaps his wings.

*Kayleigh Gargan  (9)*
*Thames View Junior School*

## SCHOOL

Dinnertime, playtime,
Home time, breaktime, reading time,
Work time, writing time, spelling time, football time,
              Home time.

*Ricky Marney (9)*
*Thames View Junior School*


## VOLCANOES

Hot, deadly, dangerous,
Unstoppable, destructive, boiling rock.
Exploding in flames, smoking madly.

*Simon Harris (8)*
*Thames View Junior School*


## VOLCANO

Ash rock slipping down
Lava rushing like
chocolate mountains.

*Shane Smith (9)*
*Thames View Junior School*

## THE BEACH

Waves, waves
in the rough sea,
Gold, gold
is the sand on your bare feet,
Sun chairs, sun chairs
Lying in the sun,
Lighthouse, lighthouse
red and white,
Beach, beach
is the wonderful place to be,
Sunlight, sunlight,
wonderful sunlight.

*Johnita Francis (8)*
*Thames View Junior School*


## TIGER

Tiger
Sleeping, growling,
Fearsome, prowling, biting,
Hunting for its prey,
Sleeping.

*Ryan Mills-Smith (9)*
*Thames View Junior School*

## SPRING

Sunny spring, special,
Autumn blossoms slipping
like tears dropping from cheeks.

*Kay Jarvis  (9)*
*Thames View Junior School*

## EVENING

Stormy evening
rain stampeding down on you
Like bullets flying.

*George McLaughlin  (9)*
*Thames View Junior School*

## ERUPTIONS

Volcanoes will erupt
Crust crumbling down the volcano
Like cold, hard waves.

*Billy Ellis  (8)*
*Thames View Junior School*

## MY BROTHER SAM

My brother Sam
Is a pain,
Is a dim-wit,
Is a pest,
Brothers kick and punch!
Brothers kick and punch!
My brother Sam,
Always pushes me,
Always teases me,
Always annoys me,
Brothers kick and punch!
Brothers kick and punch!
My brother Sam,
Drives me mad,
Drives me round the bend,
But! I love him in the end.

*Rachel Wright (8)*
*Theydon Bois CP School*


## THE SUN AND THE MOON

The sun and the moon
came out too soon.

The sun and the moon played a little tune.

The sun and the moon
played a game.

The sun and the moon
always won the same.

*Rebecca Wheeler (7)*
*Theydon Bois CP School*

## MONDAY MORNING

'Laura get out of bed!'
'Coming Mum.'
'Get dressed.
You're late for school.'
'Mum, I'm tired.'
'Wake up!'
'It's 5 minutes till the bell goes.'
'You're going to be late.'
'That looks like a good game.'
'What shall we play next?'
'Let's play a game of football.'
'Look teachers are coming out.'
'Oh no, it's maths.'
'It's a tables test.'
'I got 8 out of 10 how many did you get?'
'Good it's reading time.'
'Mr Brown's going to read us a story.'
'That was good.'
'It's got to be dinner time now.'
'Yes.'

*Laura Gabb  (7)*
*Theydon Bois CP School*


## THE BOY WHO PICKS HIS NOSE

The boy who picks his nose
and wipes it on the table.
The boy who picks his nose at school
and wipes it on the window.
The boy who picks his nose at school
and wipes it on the floor . . . and leaves it there.

*Jack White  (8)*
*Theydon Bois CP School*

## SOMETHING OF A SOMETHING

There's something in my freezer,
I really don't know what.
It's broken the thermostat and tied the wires in a knot.
It cut the cheese in half, it ate all my ham,
It even ate my ice-cream,
But I don't know what it is.
It may have come from the sea.
I don't know what it is.
It's a mystery!

*James Gooch  (8)*
*Theydon Bois CP School*




## THE BLIND ELEPHANT

He trampled on a motor bike
He trampled on a car
He trampled on a house
He trampled on a park
He trampled on a football ground
He trampled on a city
He trampled on the world
He trampled on the universe
He trampled on the stars
And he is still trampling!

*Robert Jones  (9)*
*Theydon Bois CP School*

## THE BOGUS BOO

There is a bogus boo who walked through the night
And moans to the passers by.
He smells well sweet.
He has no hair and no feet.
But don't forget his smelly head.
So people hold their noses.
The bogus boo is a terrible thing
And never dares to fight.
The bogus boo has terrible food
And don't forget to smell.
The bogus boo has terrible smells and
You better run away you never know he might eat you up.

*Eleanor Gooch  (6)*
*Theydon Bois CP School*

## THE TWISTER

The twister took houses off the ground
And swirled them round and round.
It didn't take me up there,
It didn't dare.
I held up my fist and said, 'I'll take care of this.'
I got his tail and swirled it round and round.
You should have heard him wail,
When he hit the ground.

*Alexander Kirk  (8)*
*Theydon Bois CP School*

## MONDAY MORNING

'Come on, time for school.'
'I'm getting dressed Mum.'
'Time for breakfast, Nicholas.
Grandad and Nan are here'
'Is it time for school?'
'Oh, no, the car has broken down.'
'Don't worry, I will walk.'
'Can I play with you?'
'Look at the boy playing football.'
'It's not fair.'
'No, not the bell.'
'Not maths.'
'Terry, sit down.'
'Quick Mr Brown's coming, *Boo*.'

*Nicholas Coe  (7)*
*Theydon Bois CP School*


## HORSES AND PIGS

I took a pony out to the field,
I had a fight.
Another pony came along and gave me a bite.
I went to the pigs,
You should have seen how big they were.
I got fed up with horses biting,
Pigs smelling and all the rest.
Maybe I'll stick to humans,
They're the best.

*Kimberley Bennett  (9)*
*Theydon Bois CP School*

## MONDAY MORNING

Wha Wha!
I hate Mondays.
I want that!
Oh no!
I liked the weekend.
I don't want to.
Hurry up in the shower.
I can't wait to go to school!
You're going to be late for school.
What time is it?
I can't wait until the pool is open.
I've got my pencil case.
'Okay!'
I'm going to school.

*Andrew Martin (8)*
*Theydon Bois CP School*


## MOUSE

Out beneath the garden shed
Out popped a little head.
He scurried through the kitchen door
Upon the cold kitchen floor.
He looked around and smelt cheese,
He could not reach it, oh what a tease.
Then Mum came in and saw the mouse upon the floor,
The mouse is to be seen no more.

*Alex Venables (9)*
*Theydon Bois CP School*

## MONDAY MORNING

'Get up James.'
'I want my breakfast.'
'Here it is.'
'I don't like this.'
'Eat it up.'
'Get ready for school,'
'Get your shoes on,'
'Quick, get in the car.'
'Can I play?'
'This is fun.'
'I scored a goal.'
'It's raining.'
'Oh no, playtime is over.'
'Oh no.'
'You're copying.'
'I am telling.'
'Go and sit at the front.'
'Sit down.'
'I need help.'
'I am coming.'
'I need to go to the toilet.'

*James Brough  (8)*
*Theydon Bois CP School*


## FIREWORKS

Fireworks are nice,
Fireworks can be white,
Fireworks can be pink,
Fireworks can be lit in the night.

*Nicola Knight  (7)*
*Theydon Bois CP School*

## MONDAY MORNING

Get up lazy bones,
Can I hear my breakfast.
Oh no it's 8:50
Mum, I am going to be late
This is fun, this is fun.
Stop messing about
Get on Adam
I don't understand
Sit down!
Oh no language.
Yes it's maths.
What's 6 ÷ 9?
I'm finished
This is fun, this is fun.
You're it.
It's mine.
That's cheating.
Oh no playtime's over.

*Jonathan Cooper (8)*
*Theydon Bois CP School*


## SOCKS

Socks are smelly,
Socks have holes,
Socks, you put on your toes.
Socks are clothes,
Socks are cool,
They come in twos as a rule.

*Ben Buisson (9)*
*Theydon Bois CP School*

## MONDAY MORNING

It is Monday?
I am going to get washed.
Get dressed.
'Can I have breakfast?'
Time for school.
The bell is going to ring.
'Can I play?
That's a good game.'
'Be quiet.'
It's maths.
'Sit at the front Ben.'
'Is this right?'
Dinner time.
Wet play.
*Ring, ring.*
Oh no, English.
I'm reading.
Story time.
I've had a great day.

*Charlotte Roll  (7)*
*Theydon Bois CP School*


## THE PARK

I like playing at the park,
I like picking up all the bark,
But sometimes my mother tells me off.
I go 'Oh bother.'
Sometimes I put it on the slide,
Then all the children come running outside,
My mother just runs off.

*Christopher Grosvenor  (9)*
*Theydon Bois CP School*

## SCHOOL DINNERS

School dinners are yum!
School dinners are fun!
Yum! Yum! Yum!
School dinners are good!
School dinners are tasty!
Yum! Yum! Yum!
*School dinners*
Are fun with chocolate cake
And ice-cream.
*School dinners*
Yes!
*School Dinners*

**Glenn Jobling (8)**
**Theydon Bois CP School**


## DRAGON SKIN

Out in the garden,
Way up high,
A dragon's skin fell from the sky.
A little mouth said,
'Hello' and jumped inside.
He breathed fire
And melted houses into
Marshmallows.
Mum and Dad were still in bed
With a burnt head.

**Matthew McDonald (8)**
**Theydon Bois CP School**

## MONDAY MORNING

'I will have toast.'
'We're just in time.'
'The bell has gone.'
'Stand still.'
'Can I give out the maths books?'
'I've finished.'
'It's playtime.'
'I'm going to finish that game.'
'Let's play ball.'
'Who's it?'
'I am.'
'Can we play again?'
'See you in the playground.'
Bell's gone.'
'Time for a story.'
'Lunch time.'

*Emma Bateman  (8)*
*Theydon Bois CP School*

## MY LITTLE SISTER

My little sister loves strawberries,
She loves to suck them with a straw.
Even now she's only three,
I want her to be more like me.
My little sister when she was two,
She loved tomato ketchup on bread.
When she was one she sucked her thumb.

*Charlotte Debenham  (6)*
*Theydon Bois CP School*

## WHEN I'M UPSIDE DOWN

Upside down I feel a frown upon my face,
I can walk on hands and I take one pace.
Once I'm up there for an hour
I feel my blood going and lose all my power.
I'm fed up now, my feet go numb,
All the blood rushing to my bum.
I can't get down, I'm stuck forever.
As I heard my mum shout
'You must never ever stand on your hands for one hour,
Otherwise you'll lose all your power.'
Now I shout
'Mum get me down, please Mum all the blood is rushing to my bum!'
As my mum came rushing in she suddenly tripped over the bin.
As I came down with a thud,
My mum shouted 'Oh dud!'

*Elizabeth Ashton  (9)*
*Theydon Bois CP School*


## MONDAY MORNING

Get downstairs now.
Mum do I have to go?
Eat your breakfast quickly.
Jump in the car
Thank you
That looks like a good game
What shall we play?
Look, there are the teachers.
Oh bother, it's the end of playtime
Wow! An art lesson. Hooray!

*Anna Jobling  (7)*
*Theydon Bois CP School*

## MONDAY MORNING

Getting up
*Dring, bump!*
'The soap's in my eyes!'
'Lovely breakfast!'
*Brrrmmm!*
*Ding! Dong!*
Art
'*Aaaarrrggghhh!* Spilt paint!'
'Mop, need mop!'
Playtime
'Sticky toffee'
'To me, to me!'
'Quick, over here!'
'*Aaaarrrggghhh!*'
'Oh no!'
Spelling
'a, p, p, l, o?'
'Wrong!'
'Need a dictionary!'
Maths
'Easy peasy . . . oh!
3 x 8 = 18 . . . No! That's wrong . . .! I think.'
'Psst! Carol, do you know what 53 - 15 is?'
'11.30! *Aaaarrrggghhh!* Half an hour!'
*Dring!*
'Just in time!'
Lunch
'Chips, pass it on'
' *Yum! Yum!*'
'Hi! Isn't this good?'
'Playtime again!'
*Dang! Dong!*

***Jamie Macpherson (7)***
***Theydon Bois CP School***

## Monday Morning

Getting up,
5.00
Yawn, yawn.
'Breakfast.'
'Yum, yum.'
Ding dong.
'Hurry up.'
'Language.'
'Finished.'
'Check.'
'Science.'
'The ruler doesn't balance.'
'Here Sir.'
'Playtime.'
'Can I play?'
'I'm called Snowy.'
'No, I'm not it.'
'I'm telling of *you*.'
'Here come the teachers, it's end of break.'
'Spelling.'
'I've finished a book, isn't it enough?'
'Get your art books out.'
'Don't spill . . . the paint.'
'Apples.'
'Nice picture.'
'Out to lunch.'
'I feel sick.'
'Can I have a bit.'
'Yummy.'

*Carol Meteyard  (8)*
*Theydon Bois CP School*

## THE CITY

In the city I can see
enormous buildings that reach up to me.

From above I can see
gigantic tall ships carrying cargo.

People running down the street
trying to catch the train and locate a seat.

All I can see are the shops closing.

It's getting dark, I can't see.
Now it's home time for me.

The city, the city, the city.

*Joe Quill  (9)*
*Theydon Bois CP School*


## MONDAY MORNING

'Breakfast time.
Wake up.'
'I'm still tired.'
'Time to go to school.'
'The bell is going to ring in 5 minutes.'
'I'm not playing.'
'Can I play with you.'
'No you can't.'
'I'm telling.'
'Oh no, it is the end of play.'
'I won, you lost.'

*Adam Nicoll  (7)*
*Theydon Bois CP School*

## MONDAY MORNING

'Yeah a holiday, oh no, it's Monday - school.
Mum but you promised me.
No I do not want a bath, Mum put it away that's worse.
I do not want corn.
OK Mum I will get dressed and stop moaning.
I'm dressed.
Off to school, *yuck.'*
'You're late.'
'I'm coming Mum.'

'What are you playing?'
'Look there's Louise, ask her.'
'I'm telling.'
'I don't always have to play.'
'What can we do now?'
'That's a good game.'
'Oh no bad timing.'
'Back to class.'

*Sarah Jones (7)*
*Theydon Bois CP School*


## THE JUNGLE

In the jungle lions roar,
Elephants stomp,
Trees wobble.
Alligators snap for dinners,
Monkeys swing from tree to tree.
Snakes wind round trees,
Hippos sleep in the rivers.

*Jenna Dodd (8)*
*Theydon Bois CP School*

## THE SLIMY GREEN MONSTER

I was watching TV one day,
When suddenly a monster came and grabbed me on the shoulder.
I screamed and shouted,
But nobody heard.
Then the monster stepped in front of me,
He was green and slimy,
It frightened me.
I jumped into the air,
Then the monster leapt into the TV.
I thought it was very strange.
Next morning, I was watching the TV again,
But the monster never came.
It made me shiver,
I don't know why,
But I am sure I saw him creeping by.

*Georgina Rutter  (9)*
*Theydon Bois CP School*


## GLUE

When glue gets spilt,
it sticks to everything.
When glue gets spilt,
it sticks to me.
When glue gets spilt,
it's all sticky.
When glue gets spilt,
it gets cleaned up.
When glue gets spilt,
it sticks to me and you.

*Hayley Jones  (7)*
*Theydon Bois CP School*

## PARENTS' EVENING

All day I worry what teacher will say,
Supposing she makes up loads of lies.

All day I worry what teacher will say,
Supposing she says my brain is full of squashed flies.

All day I worry what teacher will say,
Supposing she says I don't work hard enough.

All day I worry what teacher will say,
Supposing she says I have to go to boarding school.

At the end of the day at 5.30 my parents came,
Luckily they brought me.
I hid in the cloakroom to listen to what she said.
It was dreadful.
The words she used are too rude, they cannot be written.

*Matthew Curtis (8)*
*Theydon Bois CP School*


## TEACHER TROUBLE

Teacher trouble,
Some shout.

Teacher trouble,
Some are strict.

Teacher trouble,
Some make you do hard work.

*Thomas Rendell (7)*
*Theydon Bois CP School*

# IT

It was big, it was tall,
It wasn't tiny, it wasn't small.
It was round, it was fat,
Just like a normal cat.
I even offered it a sweet,
But then turned back and saw its feet.
It had eyes which poked out of its head,
I told my mother, 'Nonsense' she said.
I told everyone I met,
I told the police, I phoned the vet.

But no one believed me!

Then it came out of its lair,
Everybody began to stare.
Nobody could believe their eyes,
It was such a big surprise!
It was so frightening, as big as a tree,
But it had a brain the size of a pea.
Its arms were brown and hairy too
It turned to the vet and said 'How do you do?'
Everybody fell down as if they were dead,
But I turned round and said,

'But you didn't believe me!'

*Emma Suckling  (9)*
*Theydon Bois CP School*

## IN THE JUNGLE

In the jungle,
Lions roar with their claws.
In the jungle,
Elephants blow and make sounds
Like a trumpet.
In the jungle
Alligators snap making a sound like a rap.
In the jungle
Fish fly to the sky.
In the jungle
Animals sleep.

*Rebecca Bales  (8)*
*Theydon Bois CP School*


## BOOKS

Books, books,
they are lovely
to read.

Books, books,
some make you laugh,
some make you sleep.

Books, books
are fun
to read.

*Lucy Mason  (8)*
*Theydon Bois CP School*

## THE FOUR SEASONS

Spring.
Lambs leap in the fresh new made air.
Tree shoots bud from the grassy green floor.
Winter hath passed when snow falls did scare.
Squirrels, fawns, birds all cry for some more.

Summer.
Children play in their pools with ice lollies.
Mothers book holidays for June or July.
While others stay in to dress up their dollies.
Chicks of the sparrows soon know how to fly.

Autumn.
Summer has come and gone quite so soon.
Fathers spend time in their pot sheds.
Mothers do ironing all afternoon.
Children walk dogs with hats on their heads.

Winter.
Santa is coming.
It's here again.

*Louise Nunn  (9)*
*Theydon Bois CP School*


## MY PET HAMSTER

My pet hamster
is very fluffy.

My pet hamster
is black eyed.

My pet hamster
is so sweet.

*Charlotte Davey  (8)*
*Theydon Bois CP School*

## THE BALL

It was black, it was white,
It was round, it was fat,
It was brown with mud,
It rolled around the pitch,
It's really cool,
I had to show my friends,
They would love it,
I couldn't find my friends,
I'll have to wait till tomorrow,
Hey man,
Look at this,
'Wow, it's really cool,'
Everybody loved it,
Then it rolled in the road,
*Oh no!*
It's burst, what can I do,
I better pump it up,
*Phew* it's OK again,
The ball is really cool.

*Ben Pearce (9)*
*Theydon Bois CP School*


## CANDLES

Candles are waxy,
Candles are bright,
Candles are drippy,
Candles shine in the night,
Candles are wavy,
Candles are hot,
Candles are smelly,
Candles shine in the night.

*Adam Knight (9)*
*Theydon Bois CP School*

## I ONCE SAW

I once saw a bunny,
Who was laying on its tummy,
His nose was a little runny,
He had lots of money,
Oh what a rich bunny.

I once saw a cat,
Who was chasing a rat,
Wearing a black hat,
Oh what a funny sight.

I once saw a dog,
Who was chasing a hedgehog,
He got in a log,
And saw a bigger dog,
Oh what a fright he had.

I once saw a mouse,
In his little house,
He was munching on some toast,
While being a host,
Oh what a hard job.

*Siobhan Brooker (9)*
*Westerings Primary School*


## THE WIND

The wind, the wind,
Blow, blow his coat off.
The sun, the sun,
Blaze, blaze, make him take his coat off.
The rain, the rain,
Pit, pat, pit, pat on his coat.

*Claire Maslen (8)*
*Westerings Primary School*

## MY LITTLE GHOST

'Oh! Look at that, it's twelve 'o clock
It's time for the ghostly hour.'
'But Mum, can I have a sweet, just a little treat,
Anything with peanuts or chocolate will do.'
'Don't be silly, ghosts don't eat.'
'Mum I've got a headache, a pain in my head.
My head's too sore to work tonight.'
'Don't be silly, ghosts don't feel.'
'But I don't want to go out tonight.
I'm scared of graveyard folk.'
'Don't be silly, ghosts aren't scared.'
'But Mum . . . '
'Do be quiet Casper dear, we're late,
The bus won't wait.
So come on Casper, Hallowe'en's just once a year
So grab your sheet and off we fly,
To do our haunting for the year . . . '

*Rebecca Keyes (9)*
*Westerings Primary School*


## SPRING AND SUMMER

I love the springtime sun,
it makes me feel like having fun.
A soft warm breeze blowing through the trees
makes my heart skip with joy and happiness.
Oh I long for summer with its wonderful smells
and summer flowers, freshly cut grass and candy floss.
Oh I love to listen to all the beautiful birds sing in the trees
makes my heart fly in the sky.

*Jade Woodcock (8)*
*Westerings Primary School*

## ARE DRAGONS . . .

Do they breathe fire?
Can they fly higher than aeroplanes and eagles?
Are they green, purple or yellow?
Can they bellow?
Have they got wings?

Do they have four legs, two legs or none?
Have they got scales?
Are they bright, or are they pale?
Do they capture princesses and have their heads cut off by princes?
Do they live in caves?

Have they got spikes running down their backs?
Do they attack castles?
Are they afraid, or are they brave?
Can they talk, or do they just grunt?
Can they hunt us out?
I don't know, do you know what dragons really are?

*Kerry Whitebread  (9)*
*Westerings Primary School*


## WHAT I REALLY LIKE

I really like the fairground,
with rides that go really high.
When I go in the haunted house,
it really makes me cry.

I really like the sea front,
with ice-cream and donkey rides.
When it is very hot and sunny,
we play and catch crabs in the tides.

*Adam Haynes  (9)*
*Westerings Primary School*

## THE LOST DOG

I found a dog,
it had a sign
saying 'For Sale',
poor thing was left in
the gale-force wind.
I pinned a sign
up on the wall
saying 'Lost Dog (had a nasty fall).
But no one looked, they
just carried on walking and talking.
I thought they don't seem to care.
I glare at them in a mean way.
But they kept looking at the awful day.
So in the end I kept the dog
and loved her and played with her.

*Nicole Dallaway  (9)*
*Westerings Primary School*

## CATS SLEEP ANYWHERE

Cats, cats,
Sleep anywhere,
In a basket or on a chair,
On your lap,
Or on the mat,
Cats, cats they don't care,
They just sleep anywhere!

*Hannah Wells  (9)*
*Westerings Primary School*

# CHRISTMAS

Father Christmas is flying in the sky,
When he leaves he eats a pie.

Lots of presents around the tree,
Lots of food to smell and see.

Rudolph has a bright red nose,
It guides his way as it glows.

Everything is eaten, yum, yum, yummy,
All the food is in their tummy.

Presents are opened, wrappers in the bin,
Lots of sweeties in a tin.

Chicken is served, I get the bone,
'Oh no,' there goes the phone.

Cards are open, envelopes torn,
All the children have been up since dawn.

Matthew is playing with a brand new car,
Pushing, pushing, it won't go far.

Lights glowing on the Christmas tree,
They look pretty! Don't you agree?

Hayley's got a make-up kit,
It doesn't make her pretty, not a bit.

That's the end, say 'Goodbye'
That's the end, 'Please don't cry.'

*Daniel Payne (9)*
*Westerings Primary School*

## THE IRON MAN

Is this the end?

The clanging of a leg,
Banging off the rock,
Did it just miss an egg?
Tumbling down,
Is this the end?

The crack of a neck,
The tinking of an eye,
A squawk of a seagull,
Flying up high.

A heavy crash of a head,
Clonk, bonk, bang,
Was that another leg?
Dink, tink, clang,
Is this the end?

A rattle of a loose bolt,
Bouncing down the cliff,
Did it hit a gull?
I hope it did not!

Clatter, batter,
Chink, tink, tong,
Ting, ping, cling,
Clonk, bonk, bong . . .

*Crash!*

I've a feeling it's the end!

*Amy Chapman  (8)*
*Westerings Primary School*

## WHAT IS ORANGE?

Orange is a tangerine
In the grocer's shop.
Orange is a firework
That has just gone pop.
Orange is a sunset
Blazing and bright.
Orange is a candle
Burning in the night.
Orange is a ball
Kicked high in the sky.
Orange is a robin
Flying close by.
Orange is a fox
Hunting for its prey.
Orange is a pot
Made from clay.
Orange is a bonfire
Lit in a field.
Orange is a house
Just being built.
Orange is a cat
Brave and proud.
Orange is the sun
Sometimes hidden by a cloud.
Orange is beautiful!

*Nicola Eisenhauer  (9)*
*Westerings Primary School*

## A Day At School

Standing in the playground, waiting in line,
Here comes a friend of mine.
The whistle blows,
Oh, today it's the turn of Mrs Rose.

In we go one by one,
Who dares to run?
Into the cloakroom we all rush
A teacher comes in and tells us to hush.

Round to the classroom we all go
Ready for the day to start.
Let's hope it doesn't go slow.

*Lyndsay Swan  (8)*
*Westerings Primary School*


## One Dark Night

When I was out walking
one dark night.
I heard something behind me
one dark night.
I heard footsteps
one dark night.
Moonlight behind me
one dark night.
Shadows dancing behind me
one dark night.
I was shaking and cold
one dark night.

*Craig Townsend  (9)*
*Westerings Primary School*